Oxford International Resources

6

Early Years
Activity Book

Deborah Roberts

Shahbano Bilgrami

Sue Cowley

OXFORD
UNIVERSITY PRESS

Contents

Weather fun

In this topic, learners are encouraged to:

- name and create weather sounds
- explore the composition of numbers to 12
- identify repeating patterns
- sort items into sets by pattern and colour
- compare things.

Teachers will also help learners to:

- create and record sound effects
- respond to and make their own weather art
- make cloud craft and their own designs
- explore properties of different materials
- learn role-play skills to enact a fable
- put together a collage
- arrange repeating patterns.

Weather sounds

The rain drums on the roof...

a Look. What is the weather like?

b Find the shakers. Count the instruments.

c Mime playing each instrument.

d Sing Weather sounds.

At home

Read a favourite story with your child using simple objects to create sound effects.

In these sessions, children will also: make sound effects, tell a musical story, make musical instruments, talk about what they have made, record some sounds. → TG pp.222–225

Weather sounds

1	2	3	4	5	6	7	8	9	10

a Listen to your teacher and colour the clouds.

b Write the number of flashes on each cloud.

c Count the total number of flashes.

At home

Support your child's listening and counting skills by tapping or clapping a number of beats and asking your child to say how many they heard.

In this session, children will also: sing a song, make thunder sounds, listen to sounds outside, play a listening game. → TG pp.222–225

Weather sounds

_____ •   • _____

_____ •   • _____

_____ •   • _____

a Write the number of rays on each sun.

b Match pairs of suns to make 10 rays.

In this session, children will also: record weather sound effects, investigate puddles, make more rain sounds. → TG pp.222–225

At home

Give your child a group of 10 small items, for example, pieces of pasta. Ask them to divide the items into 2 groups (8 + 2, 7 + 3 etc.). Count the items in the groups – does your child notice that they always total 10?

Weather sounds

a Look. What is the weather like?

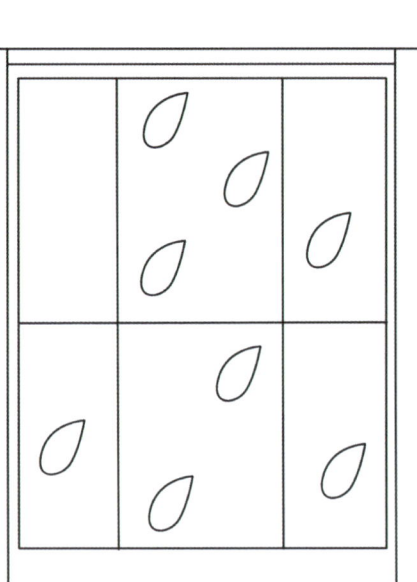
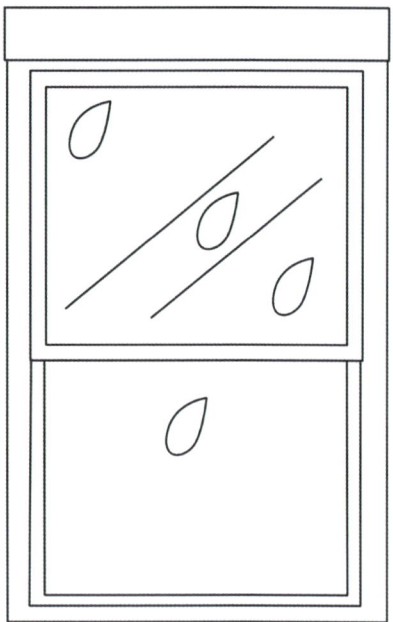

b Count the raindrops on each window.

c Colour the windows that have 12 raindrops altogether.

At home

Encourage your child to pour water and describe what it feels like to splash with their hands.

In this session, children will also: choose sound effects, make up their own story, work in a group, make up a weather dance. → TG pp.222–225

Weather watching

Look!

a Find the biggest cloud.
Find the smallest cloud.

b Count the clouds.

c Look. What shapes can you see?

d Describe the weather.

At home
Go outside and look at some clouds with your child. What shapes can you see?

In this session, children will also: begin a story about cloud shapes, read poems and stories, think of words to describe clouds, create art cloud shapes. → TG pp.225–228

Weather watching

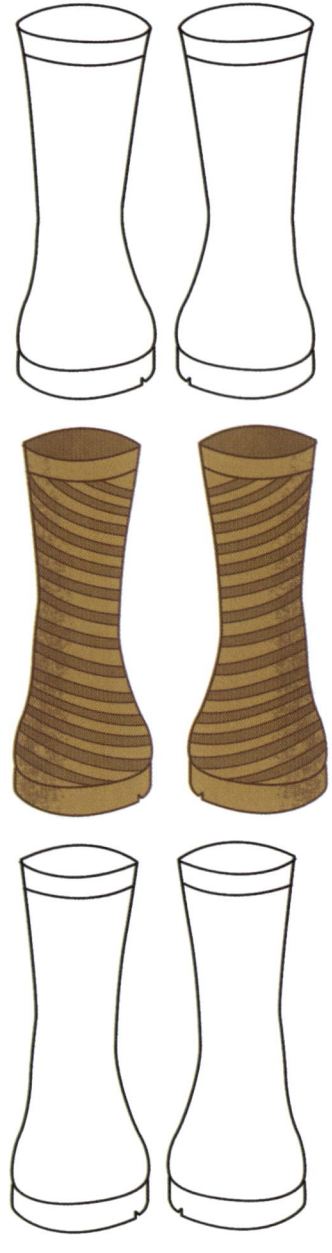

Total _____   Pairs _____

a Write the total number of wellies.
Write how many pairs.

b Colour a design on the plain wellies.

In this session, children will also: continue telling the cloud shape story, use shapes to decorate welly boots, practise counting and jumping on a number track. → TG pp.225–228

At home

Ask your child to sort socks or shoes into pairs. Together count the total number of socks, and the total number of pairs of socks.

Weather watching

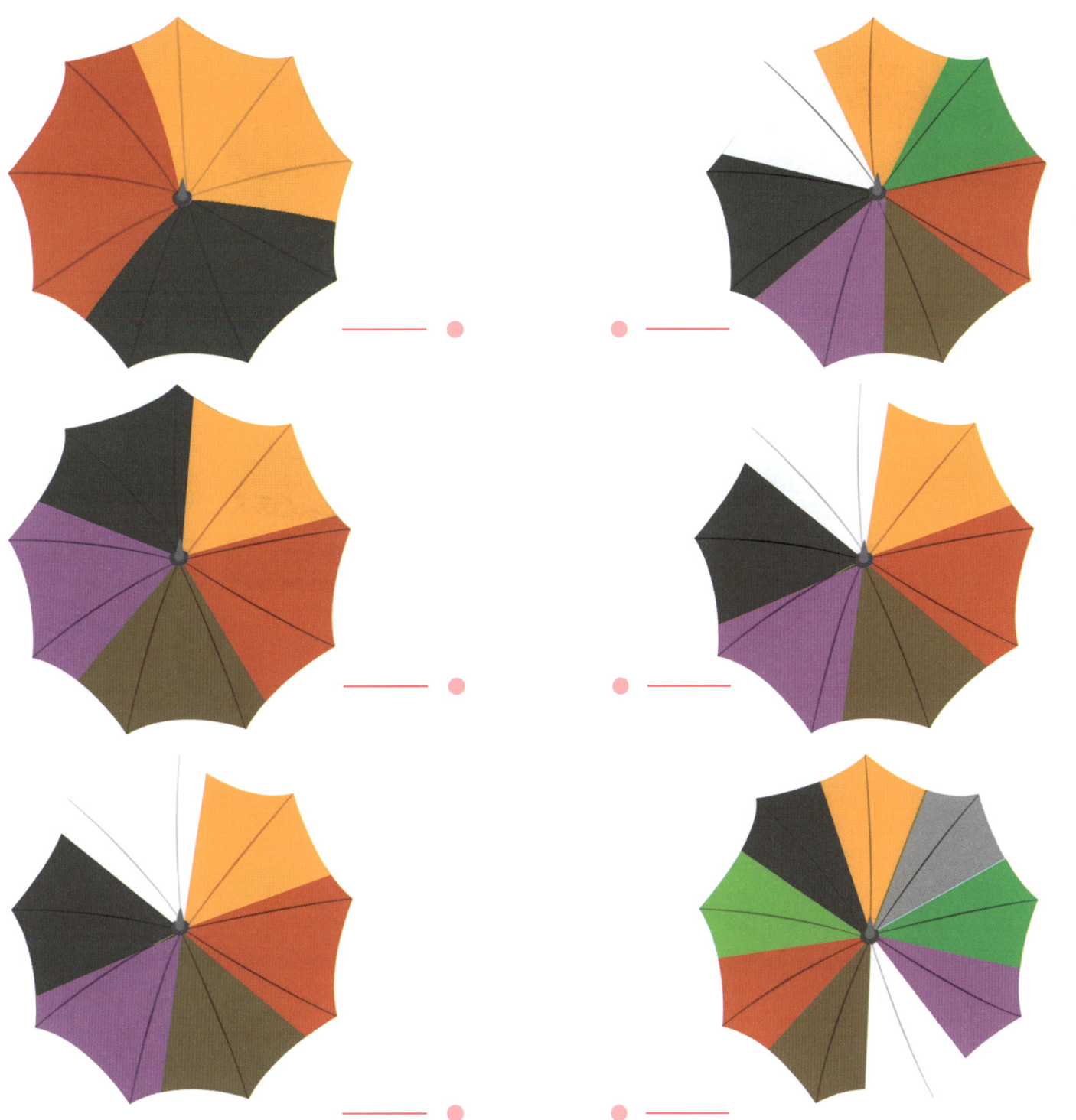

a Write the sections by each umbrella.

b Match pairs of umbrellas to make 12 parts.

In this session, children will also: continue telling the cloud shape story, link numerals to cardinal values on a number track, make their own story books. → TG pp.225–228

At home

Collect items at home that might be waterproof, including an umbrella. Ask your child to say if the items are waterproof and test them.

Weather watching

a Colour the boxes.
   🟠 hats for a sunny day
   🔵 hats for a cold day

b Circle the hat for today's weather.

In this session, children will also: continue telling and writing the cloud shape story, sort hats into sets, find out about a different area of the world. → TG pp.225–228

At home
Gather all the hats you
have at home.
Ask your child when they
wear them and why.

Weather watching

Connect

a Find the rainy day.

b Look. Which picture is most like the sky today?

c How does each picture make you feel? Colour the faces.

At home

Ask your child to draw a face to show how they feel. Have them do it again for 3 days. Compare the faces. Did they feel the same every day?

In this session, children will also: complete their cloud shape story and retell it in different ways, draw faces to help express feelings, take part in a relay race. → TG pp.225–228

Who's the strongest?

a Look. What is Ms Zara doing?

b Who is wearing warm clothes?

c Find the biggest book.
Find the smallest book.

d Chant North Wind and the Sun.

At home

Use a pillowcase to help your child make a cape. Encourage them to act out a story wearing their cape.

In these sessions, children will also: measure how far they blow objects, make sun shapes, make costumes, act out the fable, talk about kindness. → TG pp.229–231

15

Who's the strongest?

a Look. How many caps are missing?

b Draw the missing caps with their numbers.

In this session, children will also: practise counting down from 12, find out more about the wind in a different region, practise moving their bodies in different ways. → TG pp.229–231

At home

Encourage your child to draw a picture of a hat that they would like to wear.

Explore

Who's the strongest?

a Finish the pattern.

Today the weather is _____

_____

_____

_____

_____

b Look outside and complete the sentence.

In this session, children will also: review the fable of the wind and the sun; the link between the weather and their feelings; hearing sounds; counting the total number. → TG pp.229–231

At home

Ask your child to do actions to show different types of weather. They could move their arms around to be the rays of the sun, or fill their cheeks and blow out to be the wind.

Living things

In this topic, learners are encouraged to:

- retell a story

- learn about different habitats

- explore conservation and the outdoor world

- understand capacity and *the most* in a set

- learn about camouflage and display

- match and count pairs.

Teachers will also help learners to:

- find rhyming words

- compare animals using words for size

- make a planter from recycled items

- draw a simple bar chart

- observe and talk about colour.

Where does it live?

Which habitat?

1

2

desert

3

ocean

4

Here!

rainforest

a Name the animals and the places.

b Retell the story.

At home

Ask your child where these animals live: parrot (rainforest), camel (desert), and sea turtle (ocean). Look online for information about an animal.

In this session, children will also: find out more about different animals' habitats, play a habitat matching game. → TG pp.232–235

Explore

a Count the creatures. Write the total.

b Find the biggest crab.
Find the smallest shells.

In this session, children will also: create and play with a small world rock pool, compare the capacity of buckets, find things lighter and heavier than a shell. → TG pp.232–235

At home
With your child, look at some seashells (or search online for pictures of seashells). Talk about the sizes, patterns, and colours of the shells.

Where does it live?

a Look. Which creatures can you name?

b Listen to your teacher and colour the boxes.

At home

Ask your child to name 3 animals. Talk about which is tallest and which is smallest.

Where does it live?

a Match the place to the right animal.

b Draw a place for a cat to sleep.

In this session, children will also: talk about the best habitat for a pet cat, find out about creatures that live in caves, explore echoes. → TG pp.232–235

At home

Take your child outdoors. What can they hear, see, and smell? What is the same and what is different from being indoors?

Where does it live?

a Find the living things.

Plants _____

Creatures _____

b Look and write the numbers.

In this session, children will also: talk about their own homes, create a block graph about favourite habitats, observe a local habitat. → TG pp.232–235

At home

Choose an indoor or outdoor space and sit quietly together. Talk with your child about what you hear (e.g. footsteps, natural sounds, traffic, etc.).

How can we help?

Wow!

We are helping.

a Look. Which animals can you name?

b Name the animal that needs help.

c Count the plastic bottles.

d Find the fullest bag.

At home

Ask your child to help you sort paper, plastic, and glass packaging into piles for recycling.

In these sessions, children will also: hear a story, predict what will happen next, learn more about seaside habitats, learn the phrase 'reduce, reuse, recycle'. → TG pp.235–238

Explore

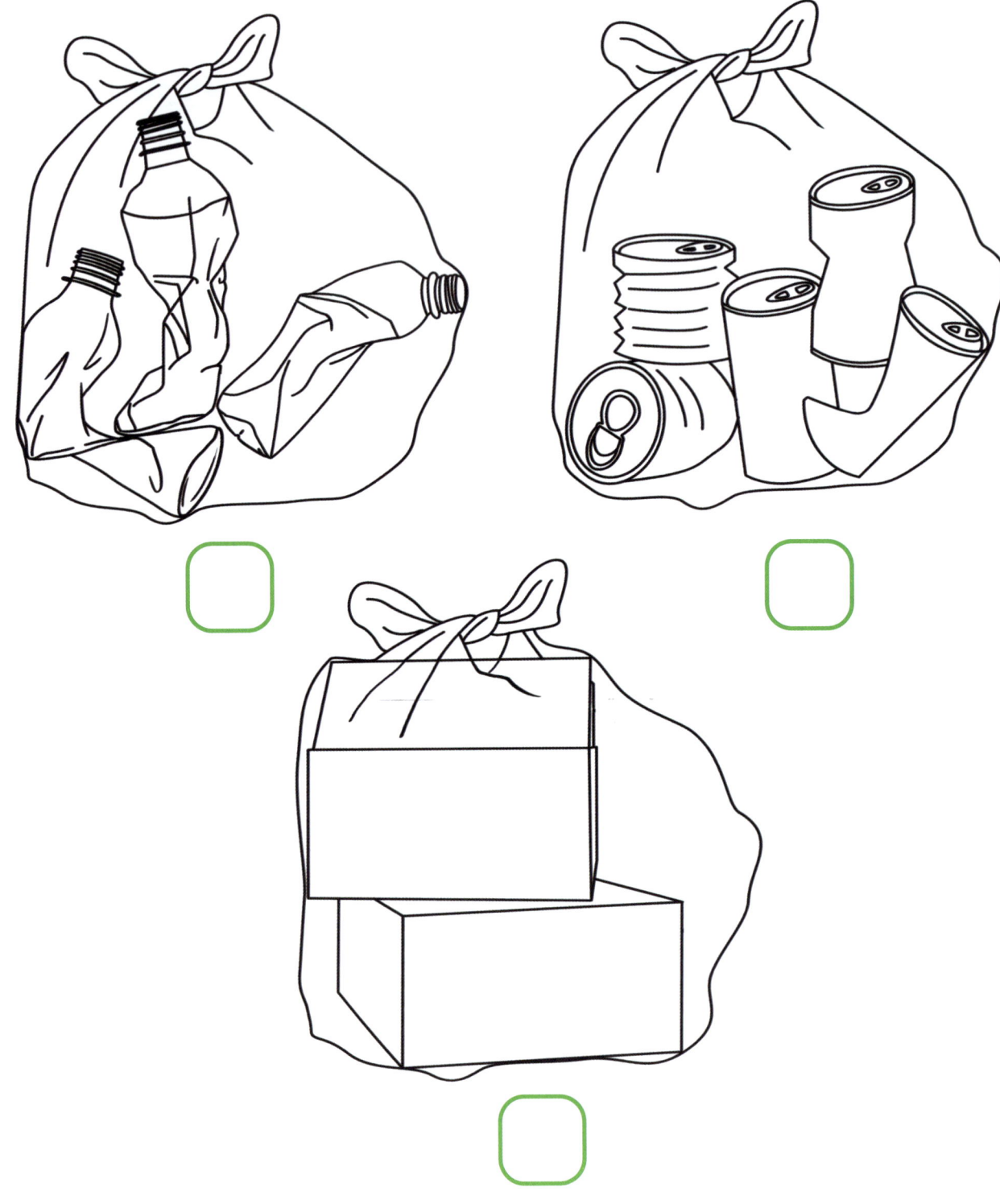

a Tick (✔) the bag with the most things in it.

b Colour the biggest things ✹ and the smallest things ✸.

In this session, children will also: sort items for recycling, reuse plastic bottles for a skittles game, compare bottles that are full, half full, and empty. → TG pp.235–238

At home

With your child, gather some recycled materials (e.g. yogurt pots, cartons). Think about ways to reuse them.

How can we help?

1   **2**   **3**   **4**   **5**

a Say the number of worms in each bin.

b Match each picture to the right number.

c Circle the bin with the most worms.

At home

With your child, dig a hole to find worms or other creatures in the soil or compost. Count how many creatures that you find.

In this session, children will also: learn what a composter does, find out about earthworms, make a mini-composter, design a poster about 'reduce, reuse, recycle'. → TG pp.235–238

Connect

1

2

a Look. What is the same in pictures 1 and 2?
What is different?

b Count the people. Count the animals.

In this session, children will also: talk about places that are special in their community, plan and take part in a local cleaning-up activity. → TG pp.235–238

At home

Talk to your child about disposing of litter responsibly. Why is it important for the community?

Can you see it?

Where is it?

a Find the chameleon.

b Name the colours on the frog.

c Look. How are the animals different?

d Sing All my colours.

Engage

At home

Ask your child to choose a favourite animal, and look up some information about it online. Ask them to draw, colour, and label a picture of it.

In this session, children will also: find out more about chameleons, colour a chameleon to match a place in the room. → TG pp.239–241

Can you see it?

a Say the total number of chameleons.

b Draw lines to match the pairs.

c Say how many pairs there are.

At home

Look around your home for coloured patterns that you can count. Ask your child, for example, 'how many red stripes?' or 'how many blue spots?'.

In this session, children will also: find out about poison dart frogs, make and compare groups of frogs, play an 'I spy' game with colours. → TG pp.239–241

Can you see it?

☐   ☐   ☐

a Say the number of stripes you can see.

b Tick (✓) the insect with most stripes.

c Count and colour the spots .

At home

With your child, observe some insects in your garden or at the park. Talk about the colours of these insects and what noises they make.

Can you see it?

a Find the insect.

b Colour the monkey 🟤.

c Colour the leaves 🟢 and the branches ⚫.

In this session, children will also: write labels for an insect and a monkey, find out about local animals and plants, create a camouflaged hide to watch nature. → TG pp.239–241

At home

On a walk, look for animals or plants that are well camouflaged. Alternatively, look online for information about an animal that uses camouflage, and share this with your child.

Can you see it?

desert

rainforest

ocean

Review

a Name the animals.

b Match the animals to their habitats.

At home

Ask your child which animals live in the ocean. Then use the internet to find other animals that live there.

In this session, children will also: write a sentence about one of the animals that they learned about in this topic, practise subitizing amounts to 5, make a model animal. → TG pp.239–241

Special people

In this topic, learners are encouraged to:

- talk about and value different family types
- explore simple additions of 2 numbers
- sort items into sets and categories
- understand the roles of different helpers
- practise social values (like taking turns)
- revisit the concept of 0.

Teachers will also help learners to:

- write simple messages
- put numbers 1–15 in order
- participate in a local hero project
- write simple sums
- learn about space and science
- work in teams to make music.

Family time

Rani's caring family

1

2

3

4

a Look. Who helps Rani?

b Retell the story.

In this session, children will also: compare families, talk about caring for people, help set up the home corner. → TG pp.242–245

At home

Help your child think of ways that family members help each other.

35

Family time

a Say how many people in each family.

b Tick (✓) the pictures with the same number.

Total people _____

c Count and write the number.

In this session, children will also: make up a story about an imaginary family, count numbers of people in different families, practise putting numbers to 12 in order. → TG pp.242–245

At home

Ask your child how many family members live in your home. Say the names and count together.

Family time

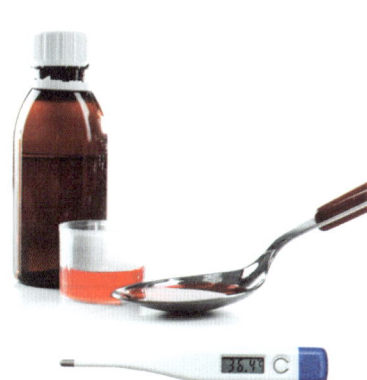

a Match each activity to its tools.

b Say the number of things in each set.

At home

Ask your child what jobs they want to do to help around the home. They could water plants, clear the table, or make their bed.

In this session, children will also: talk about helping at home, talk about family members' ages, look at number patterns up to 100, complete 'cleaning-up' challenges. → TG pp.242–245

Family time

Thank you

a Count the flowers. Count the hearts.

b Trace the words.

c Colour the card.

In this session, children will also: talk about how people feel when you say thank you, make a thank you card, dance together in groups of different sizes. → TG pp.242–245

At home

With your child, choose a family member to make a *Thank you* drawing for. Talk about how this makes your child feel.

Helping hands

a Look. What does Sam's mum do?

b Count the helmets.

c Find something long.

d Say the People who help us rhyme.

At home

Ask your child to choose a community worker and say why they are important.

39

In this session, children will also: name and pretend to be different community helpers, talk about what they do, a discuss helping in the school community. → TG pp.246–249

a Look. What is the job?

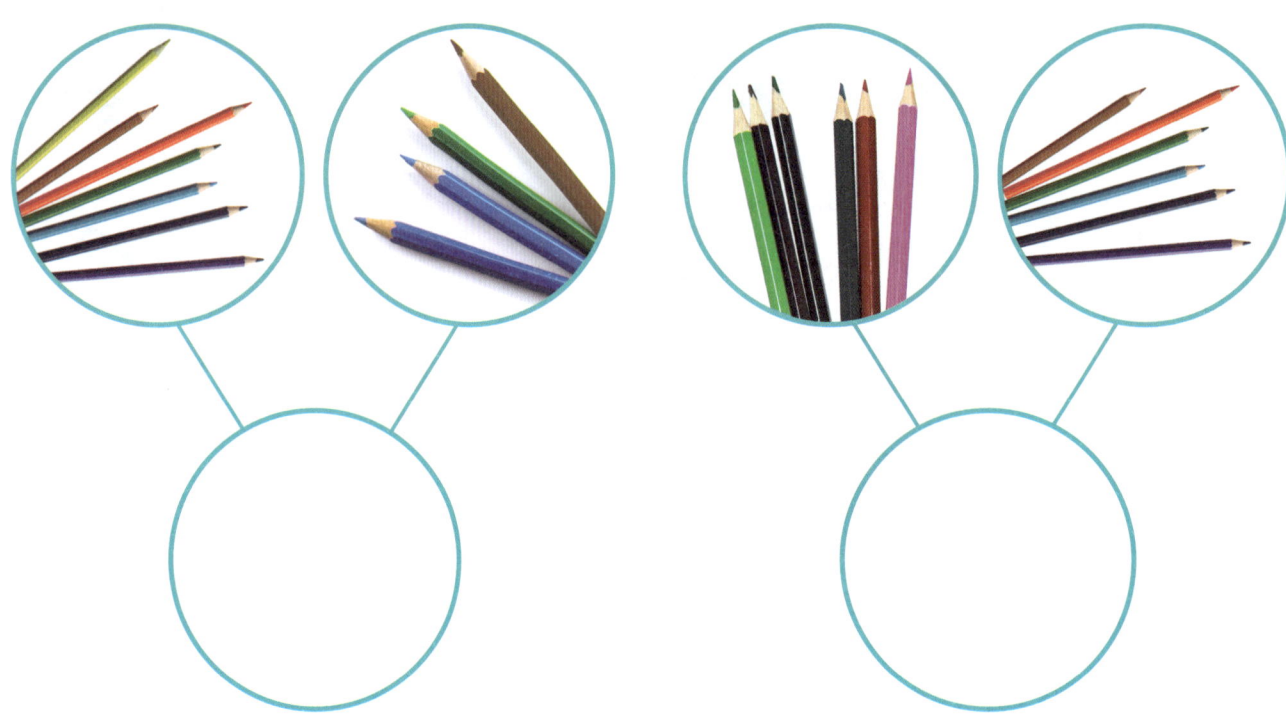

b Say the number of pencils in each circle.

c Write the total for each pair.

In this session, children will also: ask questions to find out more about a teacher's job, practise using different number bonds to make 10, learn bat and ball skills. → TG pp.246–249

At home

Together, count a pile of 12 crayons or coloured pencils. Ask your child to sort them by colour or size.

Helping hands

a Look. What is the job?

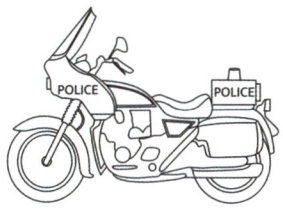

b Count the windows of each vehicle.

c Colour the vehicle with the most wheels 🔴.

In this session, children will also: create a pretend car repair shop, practise finding number bonds using nuts and bolts, make a vehicle with wheels that move. → TG pp.246–249

At home

Go outdoors to play an observation game with your child. Choose a different colour each and count how many vehicles you can see of that colour.

Helping hands

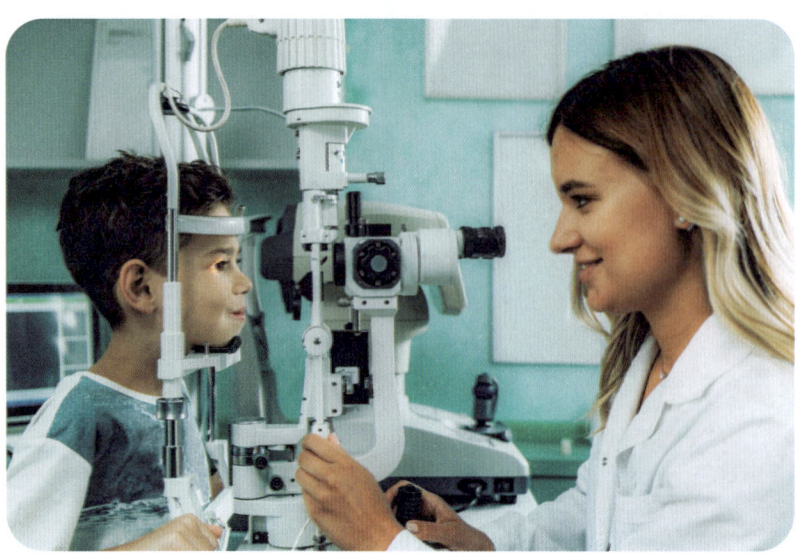

a Look. What is she doing?

b Circle what you wear in the sun.

c Choose one pair. How does it help us?

At home

Allow your child to try on different sunglasses. Ask them which they think can protect them more and why.

In this session, children will also: use lenses to observe and explore the natural world, find out more about scientists, role-play different science jobs. → TG pp.246–249

Helping hands

Connect

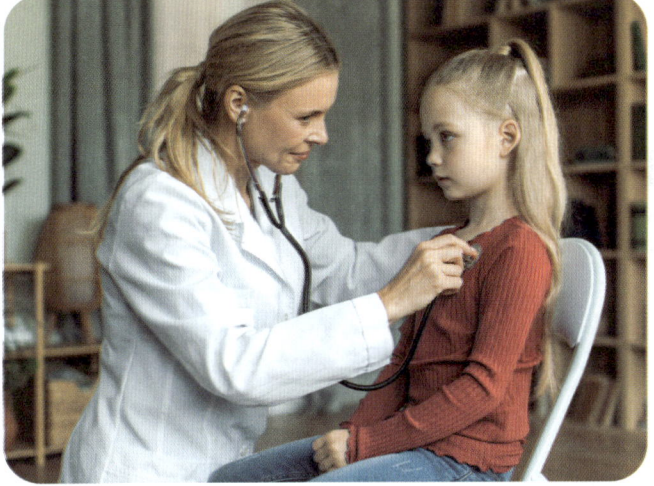

a Look. Where are they?

b Say how the adults help in each place.

At home

Talk about some jobs that your child knows. What would they like to do when they grow up?

Teamwork

a Find the children helping others.

b Look. Which activity do you like best? Say why.

c Sing Helping, sharing, taking turns.

d Count the blocks.

At home

Ask your child how they help their friends. Praise them for being kind to others.

In these sessions, children will also: practise sharing food fairly, write speech bubbles using action words, pretend to be rockets, count down to zero, use magnifiers. → TG pp.249–252

45

a Look. What are the friends doing?

b Say how many windows in each rocket.
Write the total number of windows.

_____

c Colour the rockets.

0 astronauts = ☀   5 astronauts =

In this session, children will also: find out about space exploration, create a pretend rocket, complete a team challenge. → TG pp.249–252

At home
Ask your child to share out berries or another fruit with a sibling or a friend, making sure that they both have an equal amount.

Teamwork

a Count the blocks. Count the children.

b Look. Which shapes can you name?

Can you find a pattern?

In this session, children will also: make cone shapes, compare space to where we live, observe the effect of gravity. → TG pp.249–252

At home

Make a challenge where you, your child, and other family members must work together. You could make towers out of building blocks or decorate a cake.

47

Teamwork

a Look. How many children are playing?

b Count the children who look 🙂.

c Find the child waiting for their turn.

In this session, children will also: learn how to jump with a long rope, make up space stories, write a phrase or sentence about space, practise ordering numbers to 20. → TG pp.249–252

At home

Play games with your child that involve taking turns and sharing, like catching or kicking a ball.

All the learning

In this topic, learners are encouraged to:

- explore pattern and rhythm
- use describing words for colour and pattern
- sort things according to categories
- trace and write familiar words
- extend simple addition practice.

Teachers will also help learners to:

- create a nature collage
- share tasks and work together
- explore sets and Venn diagrams
- test science predictions
- create and recite a class poem
- review their own progress.

a Find one pattern in art.

b Count the clothes on the line.

c Look. Where are the patterns in nature?

d Help Tarek continue the pattern.

At home

Play 'pattern detective' with your child. Go around the house or outdoors and find as many patterns as you can.

In these sessions, children will also: practise counting beyond 20, identify rhyming patterns, make colour and musical patterns, seek natural patterns, make natural patterns. → TG pp.253–256

What comes next?

Explore

a Count the petals. Write the numbers.

b Match pairs of flowers that make 12 petals.

c Colour the petals in a pattern. Use 2 colours.

At home

Go outdoors and look for flowers with your child. Count the petals on each. What patterns can you see?

In this session, children will also: find repeating patterns in the room, look for number patterns on a 100 square, make flowers with a sequence of 2-4-6-8 petals. → TG pp.253–256

What comes next?

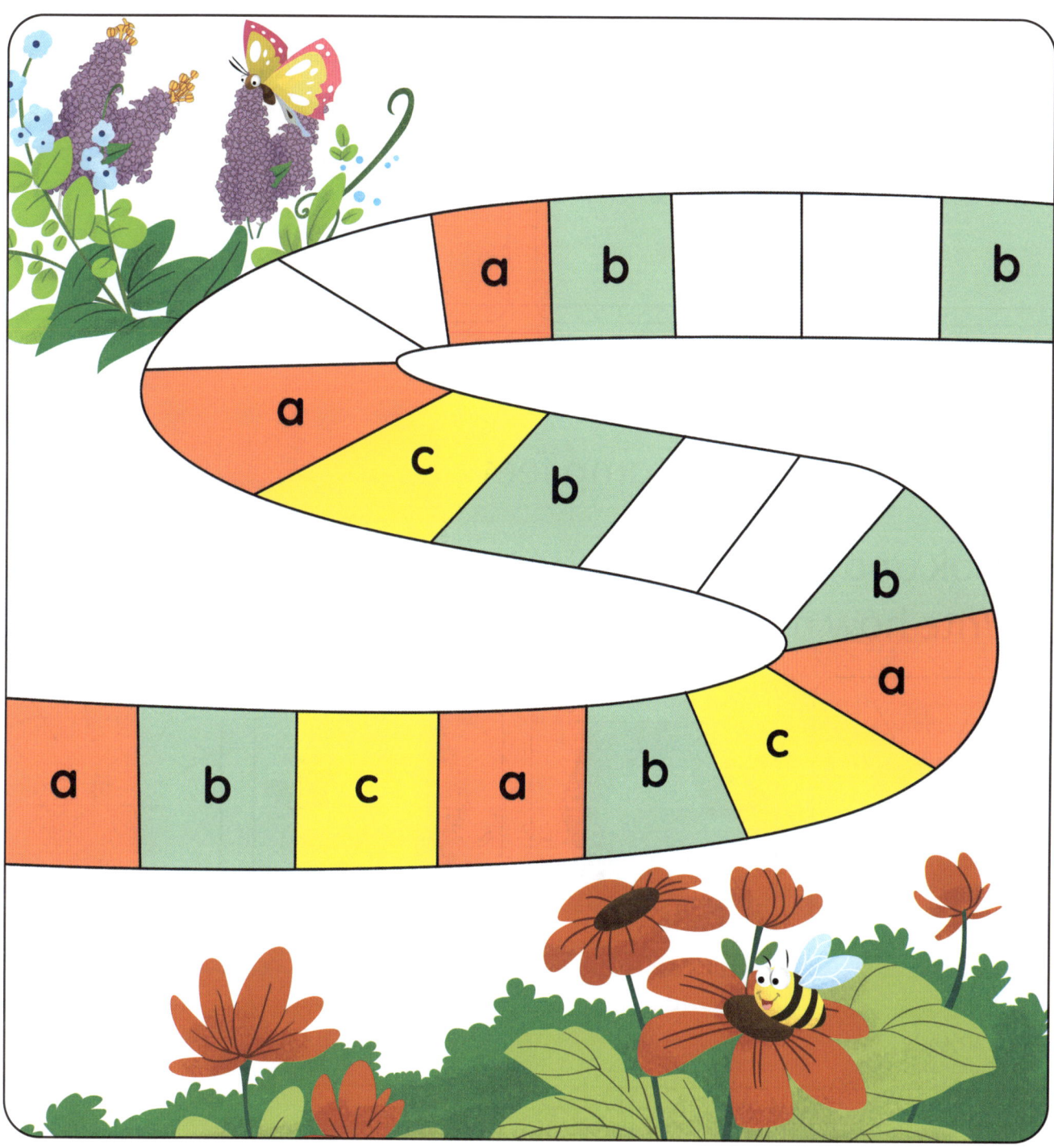

a Look. Complete the letter pattern.

b Say the colour pattern on the path.

c Colour the parts to complete the pattern.

In this session, children will also: practise counting beyond 20, design paths with coloured patterns, look at patterned tiles, make repeating patterns. → TG pp.253–256

At home

Help your child arrange objects into repeating patterns, for example: spoon, cup, pan, spoon, cup, pan, and so on.

 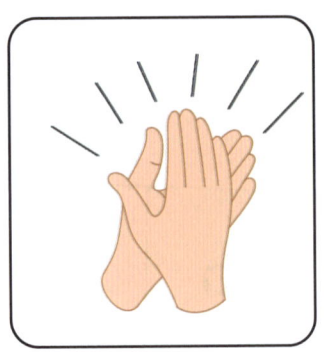  

stamp feet _____

a Look and follow the pattern.
Write how many times you stamp.

clap hands _____

b Look and follow the pattern.
Write how many times you clap.

c Choose one pattern and follow it
3 times.

Connect

In this session, children will also: practise counting beyond 20, find rhyme patterns, respond to music with repeated movements, express feelings using words. → TG pp.253–256

Wonderful words

Sam's bedtime

a Find two animals that begin with sh.

b Retell the story.

In this session, children will also: read and write words beginning with 'sh' and 'ch', describe their favourite toys, create a pretend toy shop. → TG pp.257–260

At home

Name a material (plastic, metal, wood, etc.) and ask your child to collect a few items of this material from the kitchen. How do the items feel? Repeat with other materials.

Explore

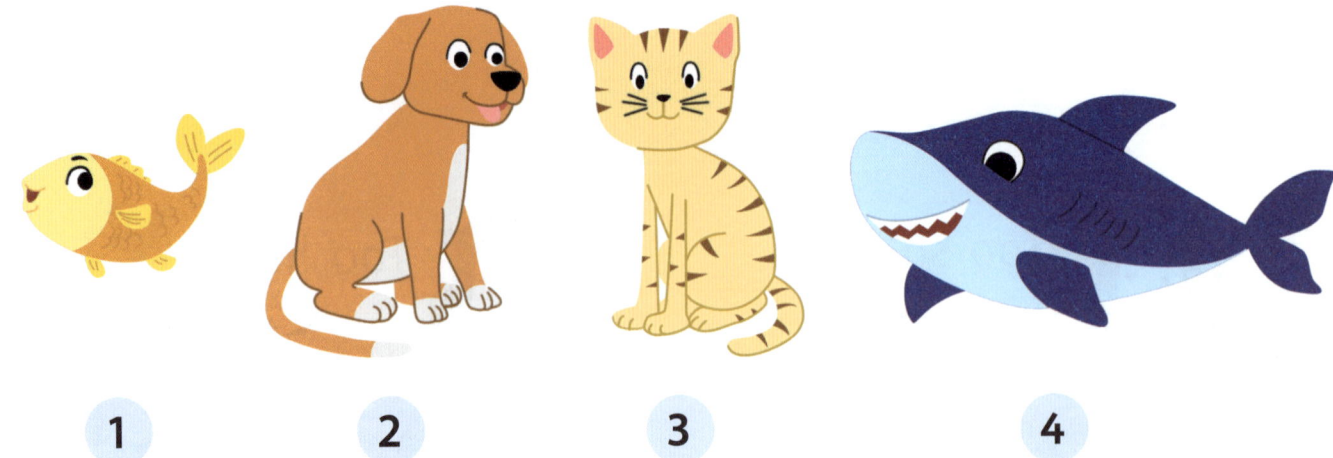

1   2   3   4

a Name the animals.

land   water

1

b Trace the words.

c Write the number of each animal in the right circle.

In this session, children will also: sort a group of 12 toy animals in different ways, write a letter to a family member, start learning a song for the end of term celebration. → TG pp.257–260

At home

Look at toy animals or animal pictures with your child and sort them into categories, such as big/small or wild/farm.

Wonderful words

doll

truck

block

Explore

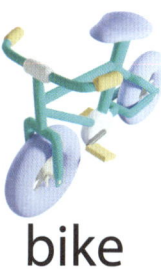
bike

ball

car

a Describe the toys.

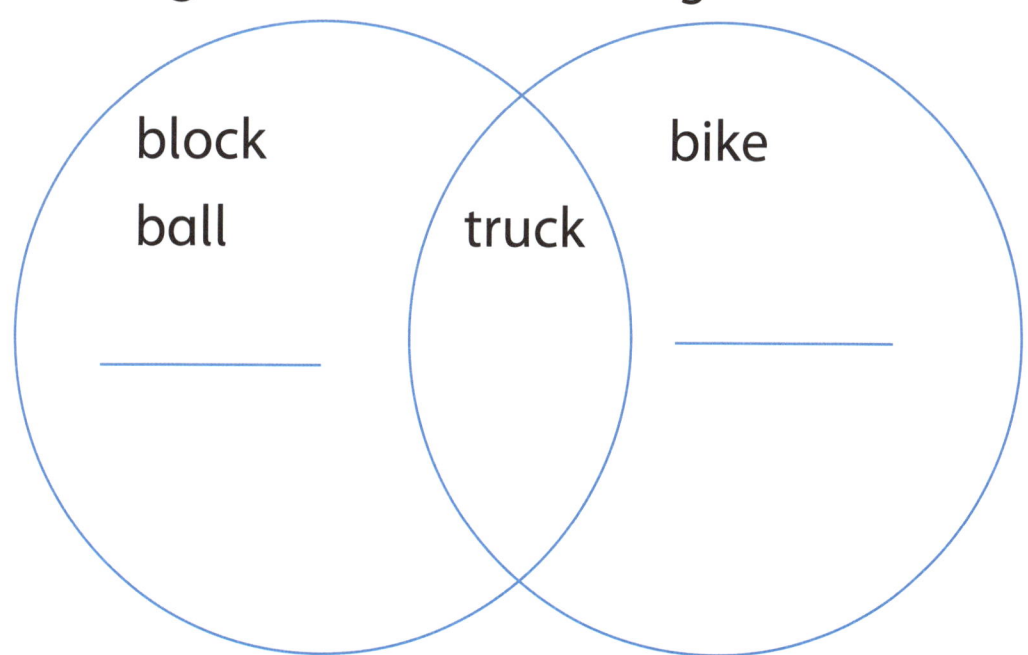

Red toys

Toys with wheels

block
ball
_____

truck

bike
_____

b Listen to your teacher. Which toys are missing?

c Complete the Venn diagram.

In this session, children will also: find out about toys from the past, sort wooden building blocks into groups, create a toy museum. → TG pp.257–260

At home

Ask your child to describe their favourite toy, including colour, texture, size, and so on.

Explore

float

sink

a Look. Which things might sink?
Which things might float?

b Trace the words.

c Match the objects to the right word.

In this session, children will also: find out about toys that float, make their own floating toy, make up actions to help learn new words. → TG pp.257–260

At home

Test some objects with your child using a small container with water. Which sink? Which float?

Wonderful words

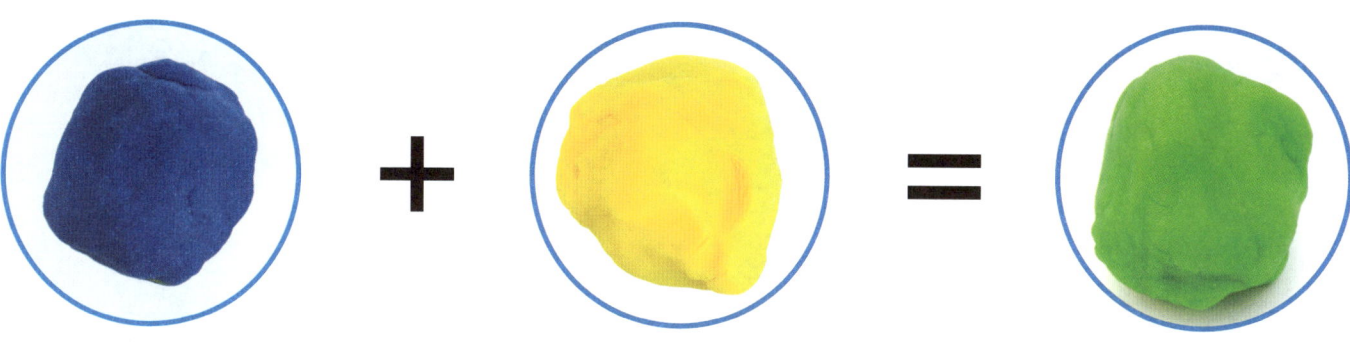

a Say the colours.

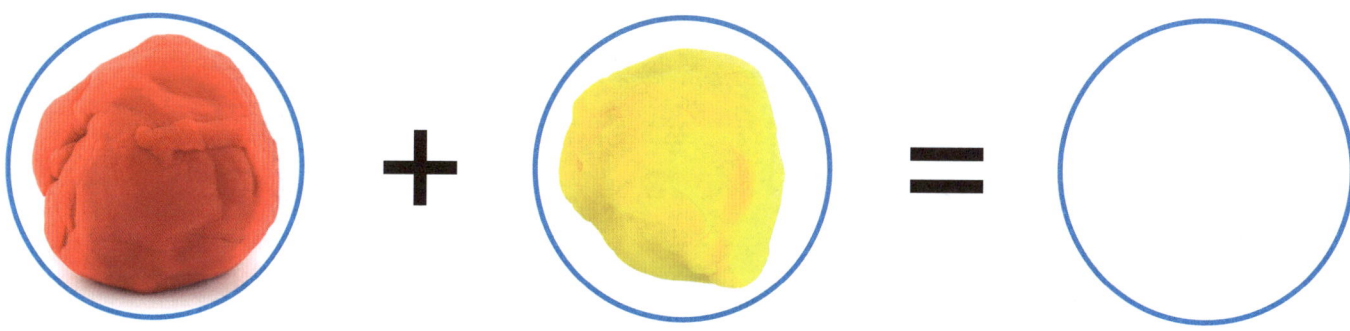

b Mix red and yellow. Colour the result.

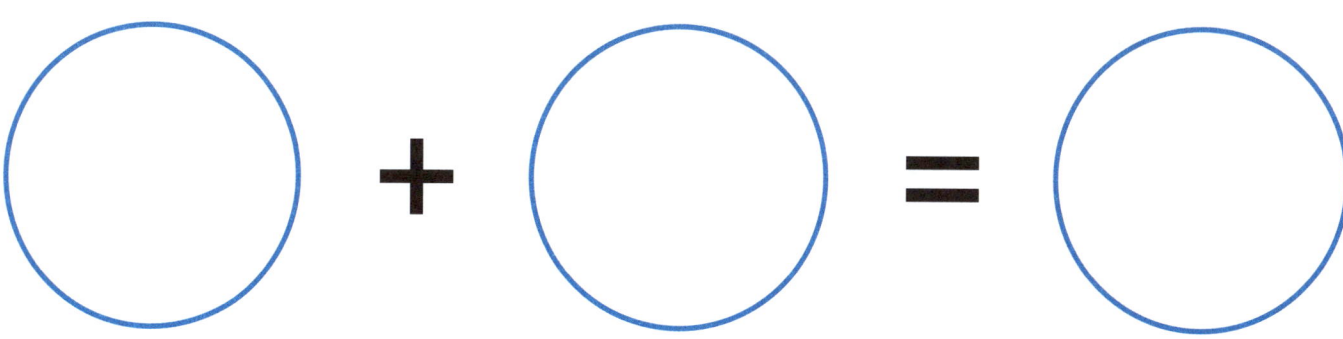

c Mix 2 other colours.
Show what colour you made.

At home
Ask your child about the colours and textures of favourite objects, such as soft and hard toys.

a Look. What are the children doing?

b Find your favourite character.

c Count the children on stage.

d Sing the End of the year song.

At home
Help your child memorize their favourite nursery rhyme. Optionally, they can dress up and recite it to the family.

In these sessions, children will also: add music and movement to the 'End of the year' song, reflect on their learning, create a gallery of things they have made. → TG pp.260–264

a Name each shape.

| 1 | 2 | 3 | 4 | 5 | 6 | | 8 | 9 | | 11 | 12 | 13 | | 15 | 16 | 17 | | 19 | |

b Find the missing numbers. Say the sequence.

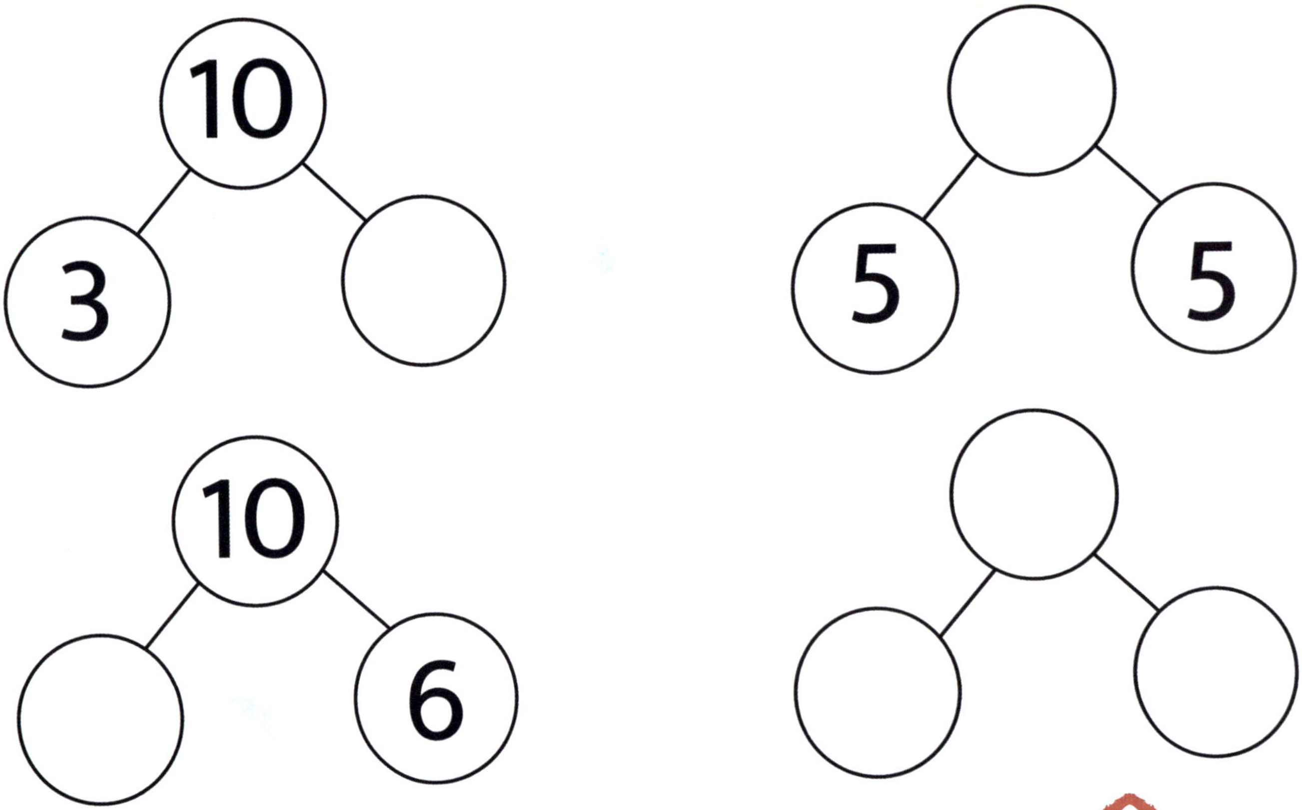

10
3

5 5

10
    6

Explore

c Complete the number bonds.

In this session, children will also: play a number bonds game, compare the size and capacity of different containers, reflect on their learning in maths. → TG pp.260–264

At home
Count together with your child to see how high they can count. Praise them for their effort and progress!

Explore

a Trace your own hands over the hands in the picture and then colour them.

b Look. Are your hands smaller or bigger?

c Say the total number of fingers and thumbs.

In this session, children will also: talk about how they use their hands, complete physical challenges, describe the natural world, draw a self portrait. → TG pp.260–264

At home

Look at some baby photos of your child. Talk about the things your child has learned since the photos were taken.

a Name the children.

b Play charades to guess each child.

c Find your favourite picture. Say why.

At home

Ask your child who is their favourite character from the books. Encourage them to say why.

In this session, children will also: count things ready for the performance, take part in the end of year celebration, reflect on the things they are most proud of. → TG pp.260–264